Boost Crea Writing

Planning Sheets to Support Writers (Especially SEN Pupils) in Years 3–4

Judith Thornby

Brilliant
PUBLICATIONS

We hope you and your pupils enjoy using the ideas in this book. Brilliant Publications publishes many other books to help primary school teachers. To find out more details on all of our titles, including those listed below, please log onto our website: www.brilliantpublications.co.uk.

Published by Brilliant Publications
Unit 10
Sparrow Hall Farm
Edlesborough
Dunstable
Bedfordshire
LU6 2ES, UK

www.brilliantpublications.co.uk

The name Brilliant Publications and the logo are registered trademarks.

Written by Judith Thornby
Illustrated by Chantal Kees
Cover illustration by Frank Endersby
Designed by Brilliant Publications

© Text Judith Thornby 2014
© Design Brilliant Publications 2014

Printed book ISBN: 978-1-78317-059-3
E-book ISBN: 978-1-78317-062-3

First printed and published in the UK in 2014

Contents

Introduction

These series of planning sheets aim to provide a structured resource which gives plenty of scope for exploring and collecting ideas in the different writing genres: adventure, fantasy, recount, letter, poetry etc. They generate discussion within a defined framework and then aid pupils to write more descriptive stories and compose longer pieces of writing.

Reluctant writers or those writers who struggle with the organization of their ideas can express themselves with more self-assurance by using these planning sheets. Confident writers can also benefit by delving into them to gain further ideas.

Some sheets can be written on directly but many are designed as a prop to refer to when writing. Vocabulary sheets are incorporated with some stories to help the flow of ideas.

Story mountain and mind map templates are included to assist narrative and descriptive writing and to cater for different learning styles. Visual learners have lots of imaginative ideas but might struggle with the sequence of events or the bare skeleton of the story so can benefit from using the story mountain approach. Logical systematic learners can sequence ideas but might struggle to develop them creatively and can benefit from using the mind map templates to expand descriptive writing.

I have specialized in the field of learning support since 1997 when I gained a diploma in specific learning difficulties. I am especially interested in promoting creative writing skills with children who are reluctant writers or who struggle with the organization of their ideas. These series of planning sheets generate discussion and aid in structuring composition in the different writing genres. They also can be used to give further ideas to confident writers as well. I have found that they have been successful in giving pupils greater self-assurance to express themselves in written form and have helped to make writing an enjoyable experience!

On page 5 you will see how the activities in the book link to the 2014 National Curriculum for England. On page 6 there are suggested writing targets. The way I use these is to cut out the relevant one(s) and tape them to the top of the sheets prior to copying, so that pupils have the targets in front of them as they work.

Links to the National Curriculum

The sheets in **Boost Creative Writing** will help Year 3 and 4 pupils to develop their composition skills, as set out in the National Curriculum for England (2014).

Composition

The sheets in **Boost Creative Writing** help pupils to plan their writing, by providing a structured format for discussing and recording their ideas. Some sample pieces of writing are given, but pupils would benefit from discussing and analysing the structure, vocabulary and grammar used in other similar texts.

All pupils, but especially SEN pupils, will find it very beneficial to have the opportunity to talk about what they are going to write prior to doing so, as often pupils' writing ability lags behind their speaking ability. Composing and rehearsing sentences orally, prior to writing, helps them to build a varied and rich vocabulary and encourages an increased range of sentence structures.

The sheets in this book can be used to help children to become aware of, and start to use, features of writing. In narratives, the structured format of the sheets encourages them to think and talk about the setting, characters and plot. Similarly, for non-narrative pieces, the way the sheets are formatted encourages pupils to think about how they will structure their writing.

When pupils have finished their writing, they should be encouraged to re-read their work and to think about how it can be improved. Discussing their work with you and with other pupils will help them to assess the effectiveness of their own writing.

Reading their writing aloud helps children to see that their writing is valued. Encourage pupils to use appropriate intonation and to control the tone and volume so that the meaning is clear.

Vocabulary, grammar and punctuation

Many of the sheets contain suggested vocabulary to encourage children to extend their range of vocabulary and prompt them to use new words in their writing. The activities can also be used to reinforce children's understanding of grammar and punctuation, but this is not the primary purpose of the sheets.

Suggested writing targets

To have an opening, middle and ending in my writing
To understand how to use paragraphs in my writing
To understanding the story mountain structure of narrative writing: opening, build up, climax, resolution, ending
To discuss and plan my story before writing using a story mountain or mind map
To use interesting verbs when writing the build-up part of the story
To use powerful adjectives in a description
To describe a character in detail
To describe a setting in detail
To use a range of adjectives, powerful verbs and adverbs to make the description sparkle
To understand the main ways authors use to start a story: setting, character, speech, statement
To write 3 different types of story starters, eg descriptions of character or setting or a question
To write an interesting opening paragraph with a hook to keep the reader interested
To check that I am writing in the same tense
To read over my writing, checking that I have put in capital letters and full stops
To use time connectives to start my sentences in different ways: Then… Suddenly… Next minute… Meanwhile… Eventually…
To use speech marks correctly and start a new line when someone is speaking
To use a repeating line in a poem
To plan and write an information booklet
To recount real events in the order they happened
To set out an address correctly and set out a letter correctly (both formal and informal)
To write a descriptive poem using personification or simile to paint an image in words
To use sensory description in my writing – What can you see? hear? smell? taste? How are you feeling?
To use connectives to elongate my sentences
To make up my own recipe using imperative verbs (bossy verbs)
To establish a different viewpoint in writing
To present different sides of a viewpoint

Boost Creative Writing, Years 3–4
© Judith Thornby and Brilliant Publications

The box

Write a story about a person who heard a loud knock on the door. When he or she opened the door, there was an unusual-looking box on the doorstep.

Who heard the knock? Where? What was the person doing?

What did the box look like?
Ideas: size?   wrapped in?   ribbon?   label?

What was in the box?
Ideas:

What happened that was a bit extraordinary? Then? After that?
Ideas: a magic carpet took you to a different place
              a genie came out of the lamp
              a toy came alive

What happened at the end?

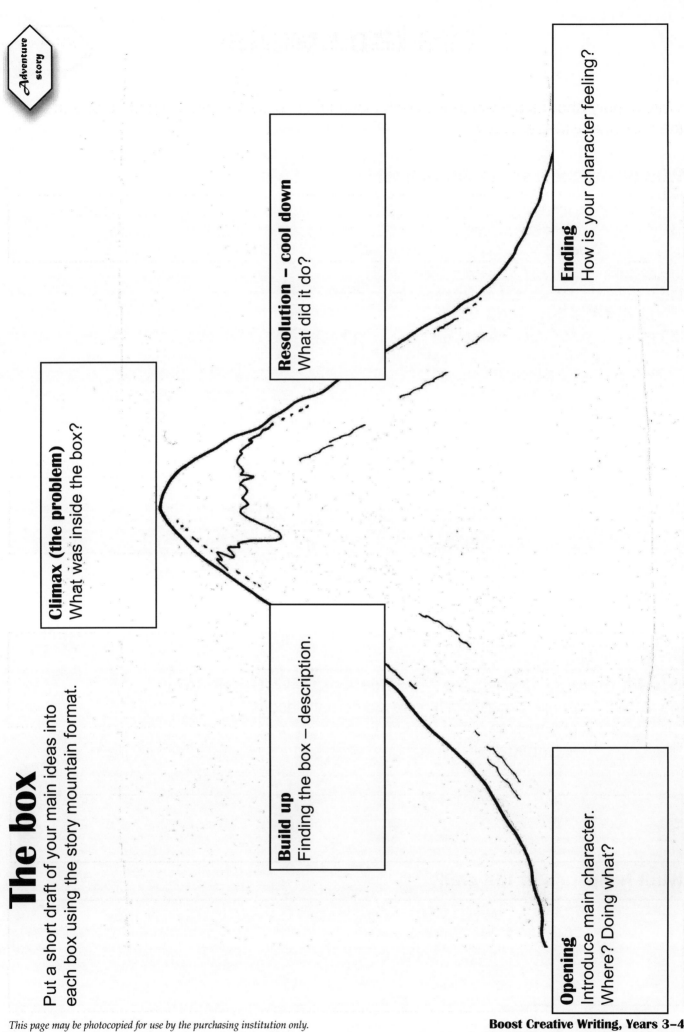

The box

Put a short draft of your main ideas into each box using the story mountain format.

Climax (the problem)
What was inside the box?

Resolution – cool down
What did it do?

Build up
Finding the box – description.

Ending
How is your character feeling?

Opening
Introduce main character.
Where? Doing what?

This page may be photocopied for use by the purchasing institution only.
8

Boost Creative Writing, Years 3–4
© Judith Thornby and Brilliant Publications

The little visitor

Write a story about a someone who was just getting ready for school when he or she met an odd-looking little person.

Who was getting ready for school?

It was early one sunny morning and .... was eating breakfast in the kitchen when he/she noticed a rather odd-looking person in the back garden.

Describe the little person in detail.
Idea: He had wrinkled skin and very large ears.

What happened next?
Ideas: the alien took the person to school in his spaceship
            the gnome went to school in a satchel

What happened after that? What lessons did the little visitor go to? Did something surprising happen?

What happened at the end?

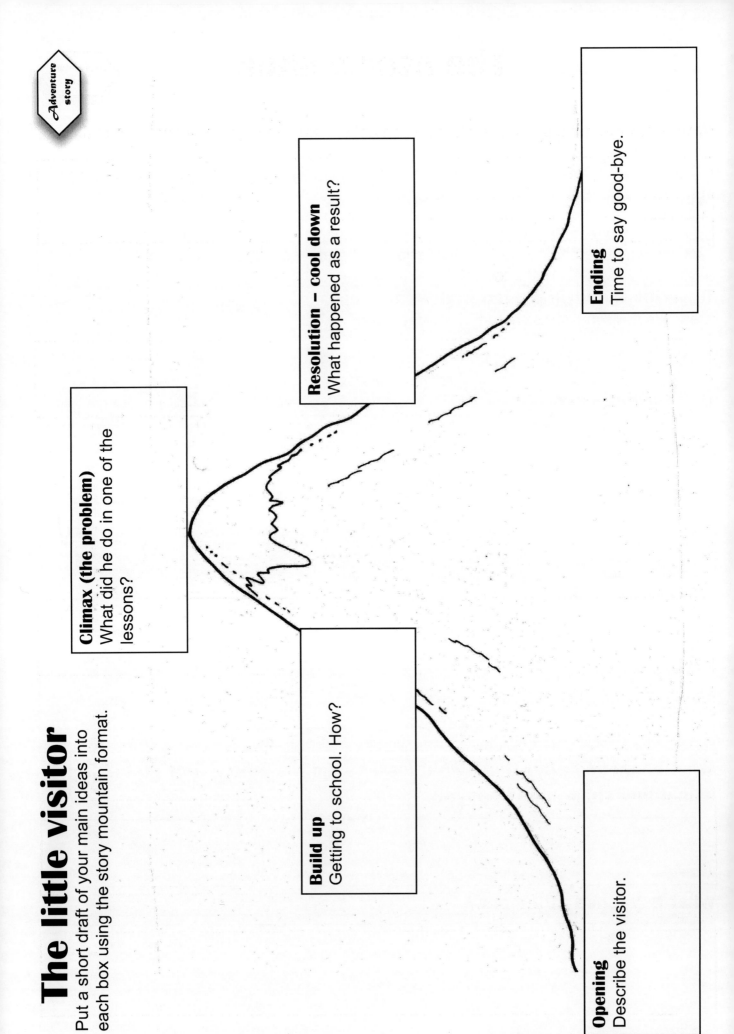

Adventure story

The little visitor

Put a short draft of your main ideas into each box using the story mountain format.

Climax (the problem)
What did he do in one of the lessons?

Resolution – cool down
What happened as a result?

Build up
Getting to school. How?

Ending
Time to say good-bye.

Opening
Describe the visitor.

This page may be photocopied for use by the purchasing institution only.

Boost Creative Writing, Years 3–4
© Judith Thornby and Brilliant Publications

The secret shed

Write a story about a someone who finds something rather special in a garden outbuilding.

> The outbuilding was half hidden by climbing roses at the bottom of my Grandad's large garden. I had never noticed it before today. I pushed on the door, but it was tightly locked. I just had to find the key so I could find out what was inside.

Where did I look for the key?
What did the key look like?
Idea: Think of three places.

What was in the shed?
Ideas:

What happened next? Then? After that?
Ideas: your painting came alive
              the mirror was magic and made you different
              the dragon blew a fireball and caused a bonfire
              the dragon gave you a ride

What happened at the end?

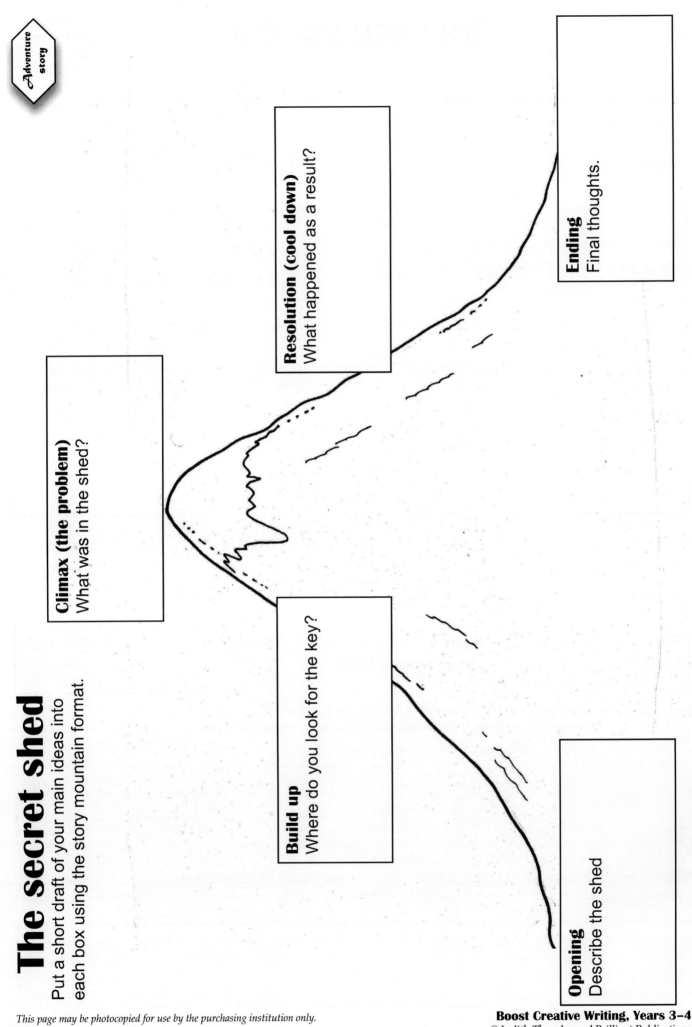

The secret shed

Put a short draft of your main ideas into each box using the story mountain format.

Adventure story

Climax (the problem)
What was in the shed?

Resolution (cool down)
What happened as a result?

Ending
Final thoughts.

Build up
Where do you look for the key?

Opening
Describe the shed

Boost Creative Writing, Years 3–4
© Judith Thornby and Brilliant Publications

The time machine

Write a story about two children who discovered a time machine and were transported to a different time.

Who were they?

What were they doing? Where did they find the time machine?
Ideas: in the high street   in the park   in the garden   in an antique shop

What did it look like? How did they get into it? How did it start?

Where did they go? What happened next? After that?
Ideas: into the past
              into the future
              to a strange planet

How does the story end? Do they have a reminder of their trip?

The time machine

Put a short draft of your main ideas into each box using the story mountain format.

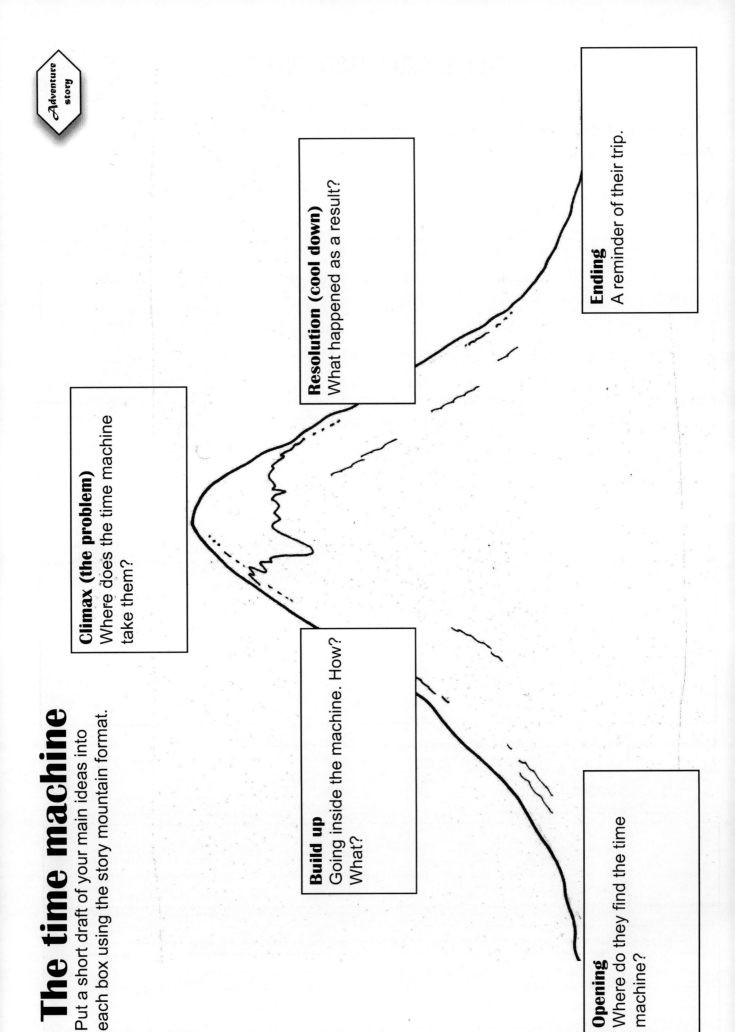

Climax (the problem)
Where does the time machine take them?

Resolution (cool down)
What happened as a result?

Build up
Going inside the machine. How? What?

Ending
A reminder of their trip.

Opening
Where do they find the time machine?

Boost Creative Writing, Years 3–4
© Judith Thornby and Brilliant Publications

The unusual plant

Write a story about a strange plant and how it caused something unusual to happen in a back garden of a family home.

Opening

The spiny leaves of the large ugly cactus swayed slightly in the light breeze. It shivered in anticipation. The garden it grew in was not deserted anymore, because now the Robinson family had moved in…

What happened first?

Ideas: someone dropped a sock on the plant and didn't notice
the family was having a picnic and a drink was accidentally spilt on the plant

What happened overnight?

Ideas: tiny socks start growing on the plant
little cups grow on the plant

What happened next?

Ideas: the socks smell – and then?
the cups fill up with a favourite drink – and then?

What happens at the end?

Adventure story

The unusual plant

Put a short draft of your main ideas into each box using the story mountain format.

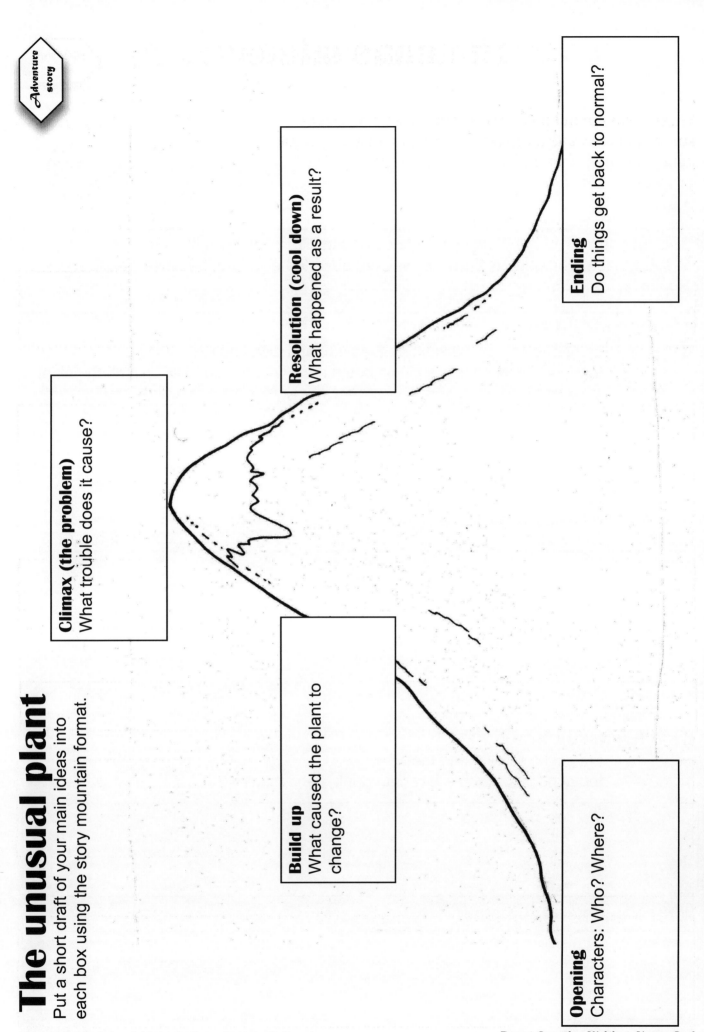

Climax (the problem)
What trouble does it cause?

Resolution (cool down)
What happened as a result?

Build up
What caused the plant to change?

Ending
Do things get back to normal?

Opening
Characters: Who? Where?

Boost Creative Writing, Years 3–4
© Judith Thornby and Brilliant Publications

Super shape shifter Sam

When Sam ate the cupcake he bought at 'The Super Cupcake Shop' this morning, he didn't know that it would give him super shape shifting powers every time he got nervous.

Describe the cupcake
How did it smell? look? taste?

How did Sam feel as soon as he had eaten it?
Ideas: toes tingled   face felt red

A little while later
What made Sam feel nervous at school? Why?
Ideas: Mrs Hotpepper, the maths teacher   Jake Higsbottom, the school bully

What did Sam change shape to?
Ideas: a mouse   a giant

What happened next? After that?

How did the story end?
Did the shape shifter power last?

Super shape shifter Sam

Put a short draft of your main ideas into each box using the story mountain format.

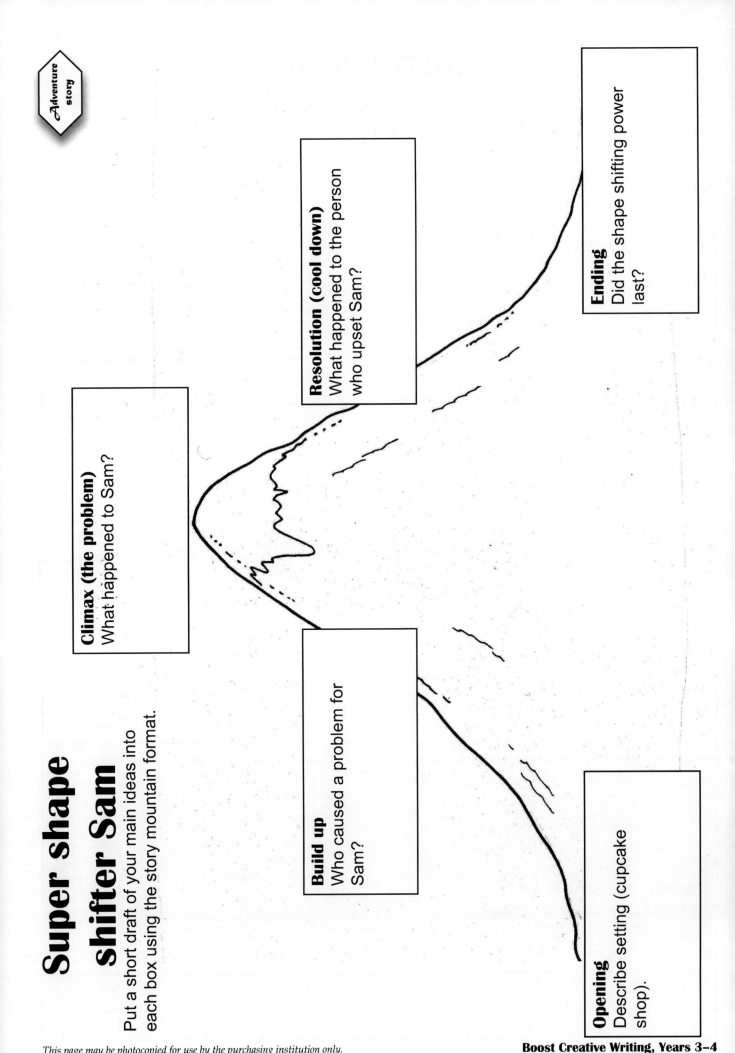

Climax (the problem)
What happened to Sam?

Resolution (cool down)
What happened to the person who upset Sam?

Ending
Did the shape shifting power last?

Build up
Who caused a problem for Sam?

Opening
Describe setting (cupcake shop).

Boost Creative Writing, Years 3–4
© Judith Thornby and Brilliant Publications

Hidden treasure

Write a story about a pirate looking for treasure on an island.

Who?
Describe the pirate in detail.

Setting
Idea:

The pirate ship _____ floated silently into the deserted bay Captain _____ really hoped he had found the right island at long last…

Vocabulary:

squidgy sands, misty forest, tall trees, wrecked rope bridge, eerie red lake, cavernous cave, massive footprints, animal (what type?), treasure

What problems did the pirate have to overcome?
Ideas:

sunk in squishy sand – able to grab hold of a rock

got lost in a misty forest – monkey helped to find the way

fell into eerie red lake – giant turtle offered a ride

caught in a huge storm – sheltered in a cave

What was the treasure? Where was it found?

Ideas: gold coins   rare or extinct animal   special plant   tree dwelling natives

Was it what the pirate expected?
What were the pirate's thoughts about the treasure?

Hidden treasure

Put a short draft of your main ideas into each box using the story mountain format.

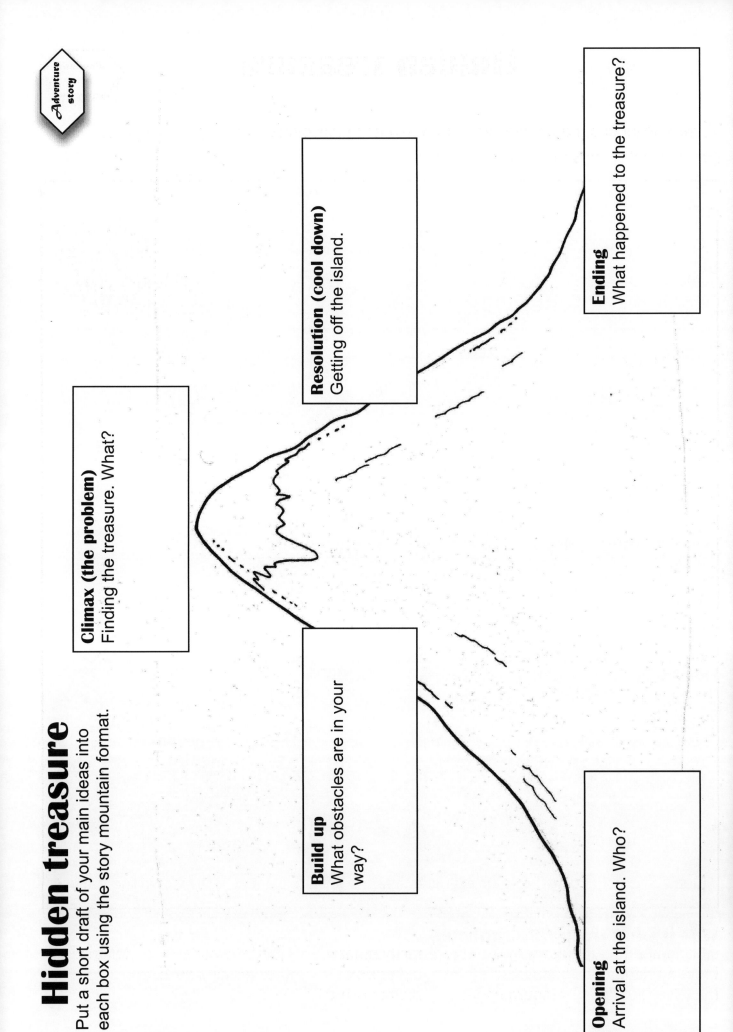

Climax (the problem)
Finding the treasure. What?

Resolution (cool down)
Getting off the island.

Ending
What happened to the treasure?

Build up
What obstacles are in your way?

Opening
Arrival at the island. Who?

Boost Creative Writing, Years 3–4
© Judith Thornby and Brilliant Publications

Hidden treasure

Draw and label a map of the island Use **powerful** adjectives to describe the setting.

Don't forget **X** marks the treasure on your map!

Vocabulary:

sinking sand	sharp rocks	misty moor	weird woods	tall trees
broken bridge	eerie lake	high hills	cavernous cave	
massive footprints	treasure chest	animal (what type?)		

Hidden treasure

Draw and label a picture of a pirate. Use **powerful** adjectives in the description. What is the pirate's name? What is the name of the pirate's boat?

Pirate's name: _____
(Captain Seawash, Jake Greybeard, etc)

Name of pirate's boat: _____

Vocabulary:

fearsome looking person, scar on face, eye patch, hook hand, wooden leg (What caused it to happen?), hair (greasy, dirty, etc), beard (spiky, bristly, etc), earring (silver, golden), shirt (torn, striped, etc), bandana (spotted, purple, etc), carried a cutlass/parrot

Boost Creative Writing, Years 3–4
© Judith Thornby and Brilliant Publications

An alien came to dinner

It was just about dinner time when an alien friend of mine flew his spaceship through my open bedroom window and asked for my help.

Who was the alien?

Name? Where did he come from? What did he look like?

Ideas: Quaver Fattystuff from Planet Puff, Zuke Moonwalker from Planet Lunar

What was the problem? What did he want from you?

Ideas:
His spaceship was faulty – did you have something that he could use to mend his ship?
His planet was being attacked by another alien force – Did you have something that would help him to win the battle (maybe food or drink the alien force was allergic to)?

Dinner time!

Was your family happy to see the alien?
What did you have for dinner?
Could the alien eat human food? What did he eat?

What happened after dinner? How did you help the alien?

What happened a few days later, after the alien had gone back to his planet?

Did you get a message or gift, thanking you for your help? Is everything OK now?

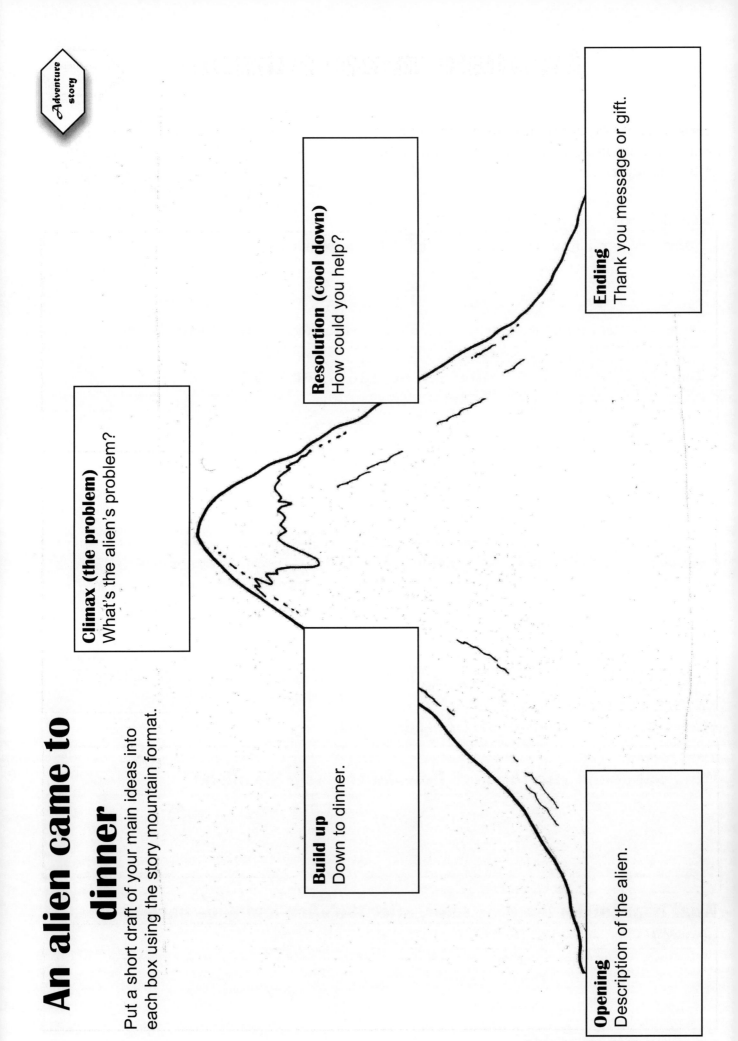

Adventure story

An alien came to dinner

Put a short draft of your main ideas into each box using the story mountain format.

Climax (the problem)
What's the alien's problem?

Resolution (cool down)
How could you help?

Ending
Thank you message or gift.

Build up
Down to dinner.

Opening
Description of the alien.

Boost Creative Writing, Years 3–4
© Judith Thornby and Brilliant Publications

Adventure in the rainforest

My aeroplane crashed in a remote area of the Amazon rainforest. Miraculously, I was unhurt, just a bit bruised.

Setting: What was it like in the rainforest?

What can you see? hear?

Ideas: red howler monkey growling, crocodile snapping its teeth, green tree python rustling over leaves, insects chirruping
Vocabulary: dark thick forest of trees, hot, steamy, wet, huge plants, glossy leaves

Problems

Ideas: hunger, plague of mosquitoes bites you, poison arrow frog chases you, someone shoots at you with a poison-tipped arrow

What helps?

Ideas: banana tree, mangoes, pineapple, passion fruit, leaf from a healing medicine plant, shelter behind a waterfall, hide in huge buttress roots of tree

How did you get out of the forest?

Ideas: use wood, vines and leaves to build a canoe, friendly native guides you out

Final thoughts

Will you ever forget this adventure?

Adventure
story

Adventure in the rainforest

Put a short draft of your main ideas into each box using the story mountain format.

Climax (the problem)
Who or what tried to hurt you?

Resolution (cool down)
Who or what helped you?

Ending
How did you feel?

Build up
Finding your bearings.

Opening
Describe the jungle. What could you see? hear?

Boost Creative Writing, Years 3–4
© Judith Thornby and Brilliant Publications

The genie in a bottle

Adventure story

Write a story about someone who finds a bottle that has a genie inside it.

Where was the bottle found? What did it look like?
Add detail.

Ideas: at the bottom of a rock pool, amongst the pebbles on the beach,
half buried in the sand

Who found it?

What happens when the bottle is rubbed or when the cork is taken out?
Who was in the bottle?

Describe in detail.

What was the wish?

Did it happen straight away?

What happens as a result of the wish?
Was it a good thing or not quite what was expected?

How does the story end?

The genie in a bottle

Put a short draft of your main ideas into each box using the story mountain format.

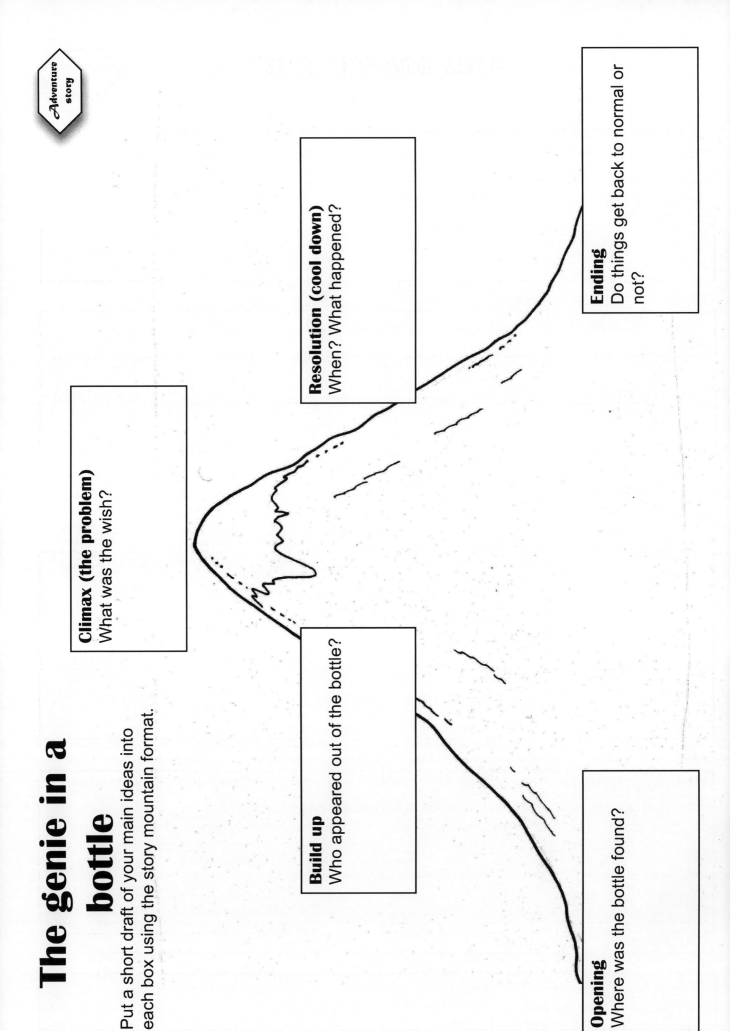

Climax (the problem)
What was the wish?

Resolution (cool down)
When? What happened?

Build up
Who appeared out of the bottle?

Ending
Do things get back to normal or not?

Opening
Where was the bottle found?

Boost Creative Writing, Years 3–4
© Judith Thornby and Brilliant Publications

The magic tree

Adventure story

Write a story about a person who finds a magic reading tree with books growing from its branches. What happens when the person meets a character from one of the books?

Describe the setting – Where is it? What time of day?

Ideas: It was quite early in the morning…   It was twilight…

What did the tree look like?

Trunk? Bark? Leaves?

Ideas:
The tree had a spotted trunk like a leopard…
It was covered in fairy lights that glowed like…

Who found the tree?

How did he/she meet the character from a book?

Ideas: a ladder appeared… climbed…
saw favourite book… opened a page…

Who was the book character?

What happened next?

Is the character worried or excited about anything?

What happened at the end?

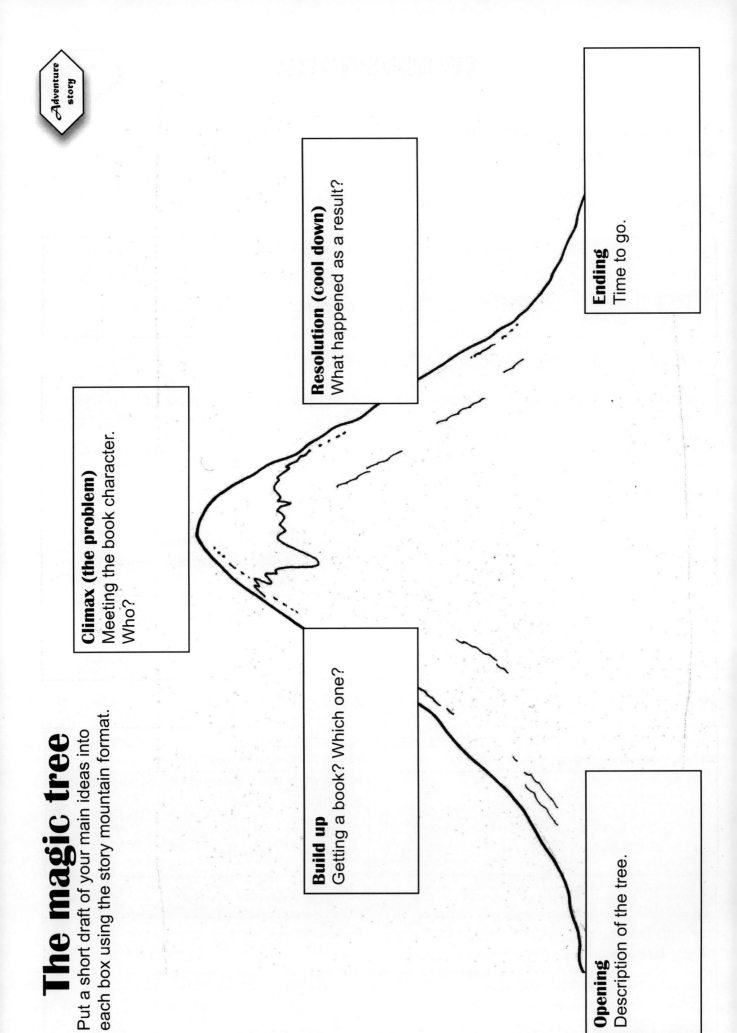

Adventure story

The magic tree

Put a short draft of your main ideas into each box using the story mountain format.

Climax (the problem)
Meeting the book character.
Who?

Resolution (cool down)
What happened as a result?

Build up
Getting a book? Which one?

Ending
Time to go.

Opening
Description of the tree.

Boost Creative Writing, Years 3–4
© Judith Thornby and Brilliant Publications

Wonderland

Descriptive account

Write a descriptive account about a person who shrinks in size and then finds a little door which leads into an amazing garden.

Opening sentence

"Oh no! I have a really sharp pain," I said. Next minute I started to shrink. I felt most peculiar as I got smaller and smaller until I was the perfect size to go through the tiny door into the garden.

What is the weather like in the garden?

What is the first thing you see/hear in the garden? Then what?

What do you see, hear, small, taste, feel and do in this rather unusual garden? Build up your description step-by-step.

Who do you meet? Do they show you around the garden?

What do you do in the garden? Do you take away anything?

Wonderland

Draw, colour and label a mind map of ideas. Be descriptive!

What do you see/hear first?

What was the weather like?

Who did you meet? Where did you go?

What did you do next?

What did you see next?

Boost Creative Writing, Years 3–4
© Judith Thornby and Brilliant Publications

The Very Important Person (VIP)

A VIP is coming to your school. How does the school prepare? Be imaginative!

Who? How was the exciting news told to the school?

Ideas: the Queen   a Member of Parliament   a pop star

How does the school prepare? What jobs need to be done?

Who? (Head teacher… cleaners… caretaker… pupils… cook) What do they have to do?

Ideas: caretaker is getting very flustered because…

The cleaners are scrubbing the…

The pupils in Class _____ are busy making…

The red carpets in the local shop have all sold out, so the head teacher has to…

Class _____ is finding out what the VIP's favourite food/colour is

On the big day

Ideas: Early morning preparations: balloons, bunting, banners, tables set with food

Red carpet rolled out

Arrival of the VIP… car?

Sitting down to eat… what happens?

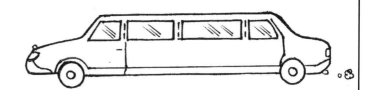

Afterwards

Ideas:

Does it all goes to plan?

How does the caretaker feel when it is all over?

What happens to the red carpet?

Do you get a thank you message or a gift from the VIP a few days later?

Descriptive account

The Very Important Person (VIP)

Draw, colour and label a mind map of ideas. Use powerful describing words!

What was cooking in the school kitchen?
Food: colour, texture, smell, taste.

Arrival of the VIP
How? car? carriage? plane?

What was happening in the classes?
What were they making?

The lunch table – where?
What decorations were there?

How was the school getting ready? What was happening?

Ideas: paint cans, red carpet delivery van, bustle of maintenance staff

What was being cleaned/washed?
Cups, floors, door handles – add detailed description.

Boost Creative Writing, Years 3–4
© Judith Thornby and Brilliant Publications

A day on fantasy island

Write a story about a person who arrived at a fantasy island early one morning. There was a luxury house to stay in and amazing things to do.

How did the person get to the island?

Ideas: private jet   hot air balloon   boat

Where was the house? What was so special about it?

What could the person see? hear? smell? taste? How was the person feeling?
Ideas: an amazing bedroom? fantastic games room?
incredible chest full of interesting things – what?
a fantastic personal chef – what lovely things did he cook when the person arrived?

What things where there to do on the island?

Then what appeared on the island? Describe in detail.

Ideas: fun fair on a pier   aqua world   private zoo

What were the person's thoughts about the fantasy island at the end of the day?

Descriptive account

Bedroom in the fantasy island house

Draw, colour and label a mind map of ideas. Use powerful describing words!

What made the room really special?

Ideas: games room at one end of it

What toys were in the chest?
Describe the shape, colour, texture, movement.

What was the bed like?

What did the chef bring you up to eat?

Was there anybody else in the room?

What did you like best?

Boost Creative Writing, Years 3–4
© Judith Thornby and Brilliant Publications

The shop of magical things

Descriptive account

Write a descriptive story about someone who
visits a shop which is full of magical things.

Where is it? What does the outside of the shop look like?

Add details!

Idea: lime green door with a beautiful silver door knob shaped like a dragon's head…

What do you see when the door opens?

Tucked away in the corner of the room…
On the ceiling…
On a huge shelf…

Ideas: huge basket of broomsticks   gigantic golden web   potion bottles

What do you see next? Then what happens?

In the middle of the room…

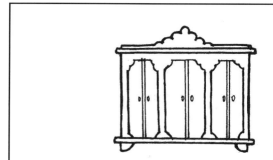

Ideas: enormous wardrobe   magic trainers   wizard's hat

Who is at the till? What do you buy? Then what do you do?

The shop of magical things

Draw, colour and label a mind map of ideas. Use powerful describing words!

What did the outside of the shop look like?
Draw things in detail: handle, window, door, etc. Describe the colour, shape, texture, material (brass, silver…)

What did you see in the shop?
Describe shape, colour, texture, movement.

Who/what was behind the counter?

What did you see?

What did you hear? smell?

Boost Creative Writing, Years 3–4
© Judith Thornby and Brilliant Publications

Camping out!

Descriptive account

Ideas for an opening

It was the ideal place to camp… . We could see busy birds darting about high up in the branches. Smoke was wafting out of a nearby farmhouse chimney. The sun was sparkling and fluffy clouds were floating in the blue sky. We could hear the water rippling in a little stream and the leafy trees swishing gently in the warm breeze.

Setting – the perfect place to camp

What could we see? What could we hear?

Ideas: woods   field   beach   garden

What did we do at the camp?

Ideas:
pitched the tent, gathered… (twigs for a fire)
collected…(blackberries, conkers)
lit the campfire/barbecue… sizzled sausages
snuggled down in our sleeping bags at sunset

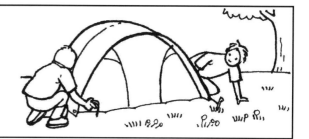

In the middle of the night

We instantly fell asleep but something awoke us in the middle of the night.
What could we hear? How did it make us feel?

Ideas:
scuffling noise… pair of eyes stared at us (was it an animal – what kind?) – Next?
rumbling sound… bolt of lightning, poured with rain, tent leaking – Next?
moaning noise… whistling wind, branches rustled, tree creaked – Next?

Ending

Idea:
In the morning we had a good laugh about our adventure in the night. We could not wait to tell our family what had happened.

Camping out!

Possible WOW words

Use powerful verbs and amazing adjectives.

Amazing adjectives		Powerful verbs	
tall magnificent	trees	swayed shivered	in the wind
crunchy	leaves	rustled	underfoot
soft freshly cut cushiony velvety	grass		
cool fresh	water	rippled splashed	in the stream/ river/pond
busy	squirrels hedgehogs	darted about snuffled around	
warm	sun	sparkled glinted	
fluffy cotton wool	clouds	glided floated	

Amazing adjectives		Powerful verbs	
	fire	crackled sputtered	
	sausages	sizzled hissed	
	baked beans	bubbled	in a pot
delicious tasty	smell	wafted drifted	across
creamy scrumptious chocolate	cake/ cookies		
	stars	gleamed glowed	in the night sky
		snuggled	down
cosy warm	sleeping bag		
scraping rustling pattering	sound		

Suddenly… Next minute…

Amazing adjectives		Powerful verbs	
stripy shadowy furry/hairy	face	peered	in
startled black beady huge yellow	eyes	watched gazed stared	
	rain	pelted poured	down
	bolts of lightning	rumbled flashed streaked	across
		scrambled	out of the tent
		rushed raced	inside the…
		dripping	wet

It was so… scary… funny.

Boost Creative Writing, Years 3–4
© Judith Thornby and Brilliant Publications

A visit to the dentist

Write a descriptive account of a visit to the dentist.

Opening sentences

How are you feeling as you walk through the door? Create a tense atmosphere.

Describe the waiting room

What can you see?
What can you hear?
What can you smell?
How are you feeling?
What do you do while you are waiting?

Ideas: quiet, chatter, full, empty, goldfish, magazines, screech of drill, ticking of clock, smell of disinfectant, worried, confident

In with the dentist

What is the dentist like? What is the room like?

What does the dentist say and do?

Do you have any treatment? What happens next? Describe step-by-step.

Final thoughts

How are you feeling now the visit is over? Do you feel a lot better?

A visit to the dentist

Draw, colour and label a mind map of ideas. Use powerful describing words!

Describe the waiting room
What can you see? hear? smell? How are you feeling?

How do you feel when you walk in the door?

What does the dentist say or do?

What is the room like?

What is the dentist like?

Boost Creative Writing, Years 3–4
© Judith Thornby and Brilliant Publications

The enchanted water

Traditional tale

Write a traditional tale about what happened when some enchanted water appeared in the kingdom!

Format
* Opening (Once upon a time…)
* Setting
* Characters (the goodie and the baddie)
* Problem/trouble
* Good character saves the day
* Ending (…all lived happily ever after)

Setting	Character (baddie)	Character (goodie)
witch's cottage	goblin	elf
magician's castle	witch	pixie
wizard's cave	wizard	any person
palace gardens		
woods		

Trouble (build up to the climax or exciting part of the story)

What water did the Baddie make enchanted? Where was it?
What happened as a result of the trouble?

Ideas:

A swim in a pool makes someone grow a fish tail	At first better at swimming but then fish tail uncomfortable
A drink of water from a well gives someone webbed feet like a duck	could not wear any shoes and feet got very sore

Who saved the day? How?

Ending

The enchanted water – vocabulary

Story opener

Once upon a time…

Long, long ago…

In a faraway land…

A long time ago…

Middle sections (build up, climax, resolution)

That very morning…

On his/her way…

It wasn't long before…

Suddenly…

But as soon as…

A split second later…

Shortly afterwards

Everybody tried to help…

Nothing worked until one day…

Ending

He/she lived happily ever after.

He/she decided never to…

And nothing was heard of the ....

ever again!

More vocabulary

The magic potion gleamed in the pot

…poured the mixture carefully into a little
  bottle

…waited until there was no one around

…tipped it quickly into the…

…watched as .... jumped into
  the pool/drank the water from the well

The enchanted water

Put a short draft of your main ideas into each box using the story mountain format.

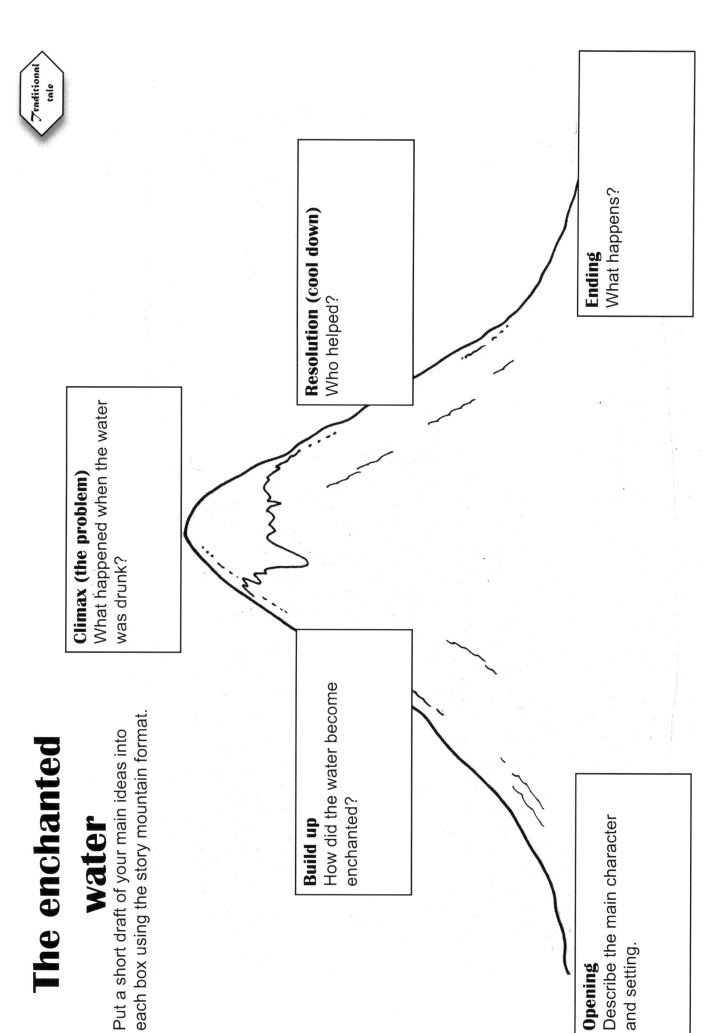

Climax (the problem)
What happened when the water was drunk?

Resolution (cool down)
Who helped?

Ending
What happens?

Build up
How did the water become enchanted?

Opening
Describe the main character and setting.

Traditional tale

My mythical creature

Draw and label a picture of your mythical creature.

Name of creature:

Ideas: size? shape? skin covering? colour?

body	eyes	snout	fangs	tentacles	hair
webbed feet	claws	horn	scales	wings	tail
spotted	striped	hairy	spiky	pointed	smooth
legs					

Boost Creative Writing, Years 3–4
© Judith Thornby and Brilliant Publications

My mythical creature

What did it look like? (Look at your picture!)
Add detail

Ideas:

size	It was a massive fearsome beast
body	(body of a snake and the head of a…)
claws	(sharp, pointed)
feet	(webbed, stubby)
tails	(spiky, long)
wings	(huge, bony)
covered in	(glittering scales, thick fur)

Use similes:

It had curved fangs like sharp razors

…eyes like sharp daggers

Its eyes glowed like…

What did it smell like?

Ideas:

It smelt like it had been sleeping in a rubbish dump with disgusting rotten…
and mouldy old…

What noise did it make if it was angry?

Ideas:

It bellowed like a bull when he was…
It howled like a…
It roared like a…

The noise could be heard for…
(what distance away?)

Where did it live?

Ideas:
swamp
marsh
middle of a maze
dark cave

What special power did it have?

Ideas:
It breathed out fireballs from its mouth
It could turn people into stone with its laser eyes.

fable/ myth

My myth

Many years ago when the world was young there lived a fearsome creature called the

....

The mythical creature
Description of the fantastical beast (look at your picture).

What has the creature done to cause upset?
Ideas:
turned 20 people in to stone
kidnapped a beautiful girl
eaten all the cows and goats in the land

The hero
A brave young man called .... decided to defeat the monster, but he did not know how, so he decided to go to Mount Olympus to get help from ....

Ideas: Zeus   Apollo   Athena   Hera   Artemis   Ares

Gifts to help the hero

winged sandals
to travel more easily

magical dagger
to kill the creature

enchanted shield
protection from
creature's blows

charmed mirror
if the creature saw
its reflection it would die

The journey and the struggle with the beast
Ideas:
He travelled over/across .... for several days until he arrived at the
.... where the monster lived. It was a fierce struggle…

The ending
Ideas:
.... was rewarded for his bravery and given lots of ....
for slaying the monstrous creature.

Boost Creative Writing, Years 3–4
© Judith Thornby and Brilliant Publications

One good turn deserves another

Write a short story involving two animals that teaches a lesson or a moral. This kind of story is called a fable.

Animal 1 (Describe looks/character)	Animal 2 (Describe looks/character)

Setting?
Add detail.

Ideas:
in the jungle   by a river bank   in the wood

How does Animal 1 get in trouble? How does Animal 2 help?
Describe step by step.

A few days later…

Ideas:
stuck in a net trap   huge thorn in paw   caught in a forest fire   poorly – unable to get food to eat

How does Animal 2 get in trouble? How does Animal 1 help?
Soon after…

The moral of the story is...

Granny – a rhyming poem

Write a funny rhyming poem. Create a pretend conversation between a child and a granny who is deaf.

For example:

Amy:	Shall I close the gate?
Granny:	I do not think you are late.
Amy:	Be careful not to stumble.
Granny:	Yes I do like apple crumble.
Amy:	Would you like anything from town?
Granny:	No, I cannot see a clown.
Amy:	Are you feeling a bit sick?
Granny:	No, thank you, I don't need my stick.
Amy:	Have I got a spot on my face?
Granny:	Oh no, I don't think I could win a race.

Start by working out words with the same rhyming patterns. Then think of your sentences. Here are a few to start you off:

ate	crate gate late mate plate slate
umble	crumble grumble jumble mumble stumble
ink	drink pink rink sink think wink
ell	bell sell shell smell spell well yell
ace	brace face lace place race trace

Rhyming ideas:

ain ack atch ight ice eat udge ake ound

Boost Creative Writing, Years 3–4
© Judith Thornby and Brilliant Publications

Granny – a rhyming poem

by ....

.... : ....

Granny: ....

.... : ....

Granny: ....

.... : ....

Granny: ....

.... : ....

Granny: ....

.... : ....

Granny: ....

Poetry

A haiku riddle

A haiku is a Japanese poem about nature, but you can choose any topic. It is a three line syllable poem. Create and illustrate your own haikus.

Example: Line 1   Rolled up on a plate   **5** syllables
            Line 2   Oozing with maple syrup   **7** syllables
            Line 3   Delicious to eat   **5** syllables

Boost Creative Writing, Years 3–4
© Judith Thornby and Brilliant Publications

Winter

Pick a wintry word from the ideas sheet. Play around with WOW words to make poetic lines. Choose one line to be the repeating line in your poem.

Wintry words	WOW words
night	Cold dark **nights** stretch out

Repeating line:

Winter – ideas sheet

Wintry words	WOW words	
evenings nights trees	long dark bare leafless	stretch out
hands teeth	chilly chattering	shivering cold
pavements ponds slopes	slippery icy frozen	slide skid slip skate ski
frost icicles snowflakes	sparkling silvery	twinkles glitters hang float
gloves scarves fire	warm cosy crackling	wrap up snuggle down curl up
cocoa soup	delicious tasty	steaming hot
cinnamon sticks candles	spicy sweet smelling	glow
robin owl pheasants	friendly flat faced long tailed	looks for stares struts
holly berries	prickly	grow

Keep the rhythm of the poem. Think of a repeating line!

Idea:
Slippery pavements
Icy slopes
Fun to ski down
Winter is here

Boost Creative Writing, Years 3–4
© Judith Thornby and Brilliant Publications

A seasonal letter

Write a chatty letter from Mr Winter to Miss Spring, telling her news about the season of winter and what he is looking forward to in spring.

Mr Winter's address (make it sound winter-like: Snowball Cottage, Holly Lane, The Wood)

....

....

....

....

Dear Miss Spring,
I have been meaning to write to you for a while. I hope you are keeping well…

Chatty bits of news

Ideas:
skiing, sledging, building snowmen, new warm furry boots, cuddled up in front of a hot fire, Christmas dinner, frost, icicles, snow, bleak bare trees

What is Mr Winter looking forward to when Miss Spring arrives

Ideas:
getting out in the garden, blossom, shoots, greenery, leaves, nests, chicks, lambs, tadpoles, cutting grass, lighter evenings, bulbs, daffodils, bluebells

Questions Mr Winter might ask Miss Spring

Have you…?
Are you…?
I wonder if…?

Ending sentence
I hope you will write back to me soon.

Love from,

.... Mr Winter

 Letter

A chatty letter

Write a letter to a friend, relation or pen pal telling them all your news.

Your address

....
....
....
....

Dear...
How are you? I thought I would write you a letter to…

Chatty bits of news

Ideas:
outings?
school events?
home news?

What are you really looking forward to?

Idea:
going on holiday

Ask questions

Have you…?
Are you…?
I wonder if…?

Ending sentence
I hope you will write back to me soon.

Love from,

....

Boost Creative Writing, Years 3–4
© Judith Thornby and Brilliant Publications

A letter to an author

Letter

Write a letter to your favourite author, inviting them to your school's book week. Don't forget to use paragraphs.

Your address

....
....
....
....

Date

Dear...
(Mr, Miss, Mrs, Ms)

Tell the author the reason you are writing the letter.

Ideas:
I am inviting you to visit…
Tell the author what activities the school does during book week.

Tell the author something about yourself

Ideas:
age? class? interests?

Tell the author which of his/her books you have liked and why.
Ask the author some questions

Where did you get the idea…?
Have you…?
I wonder if…?

Ending sentence
I do hope that you will write back to me to say that you can come to the school.

Yours sincerely,

....

Book review

Title:

Author:

What was the story about?

Who was your favourite character and why?

Which part of the story did you like best?

Who would like this story?

How many stars would you give this book?

☆ ☆ ☆ ☆ ☆

Boost Creative Writing, Years 3–4
© Judith Thornby and Brilliant Publications

My favourite pet animal

Plan an information report about a type of pet.

Introduction

Behaviour/'talk'

Keeping clean and healthy/grooming

Fun and games/ exercise

My animal report

Breeds

Did you know? Interesting facts

Feeding time What? How much?

Don't forget to make it interesting!
Headings
Pictures and diagrams
Label different bits
Fun features: facts in paw prints, thought bubbles

My favourite pet animal

Plan an information report about a type of pet

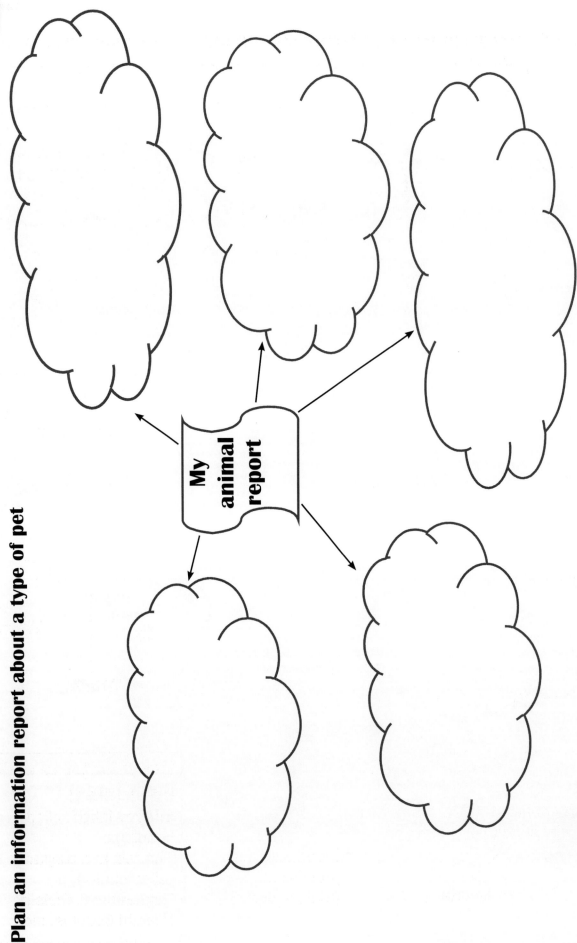

My animal report

Boost Creative Writing, Years 3–4
© Judith Thornby and Brilliant Publications

The Ancient Greeks

Plan an information report about the influence and achievements of Ancient Greece. Use your ideas to create a non-chronological report.

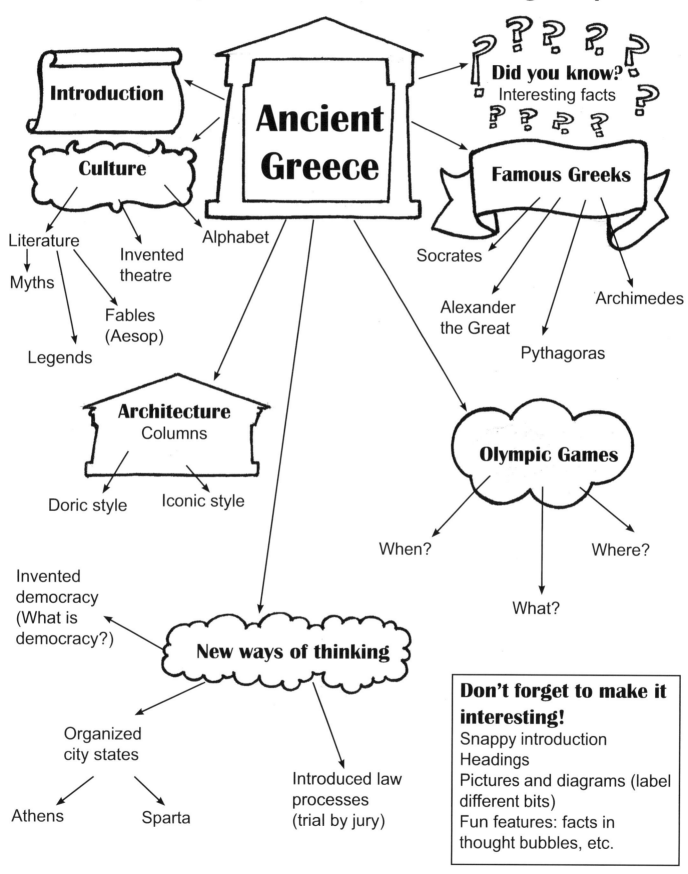

Ancient Greece

Introduction

Culture
- Literature
  - Myths
  - Legends
- Invented theatre
- Fables (Aesop)

Alphabet

Did you know? Interesting facts

Famous Greeks
- Socrates
- Alexander the Great
- Pythagoras
- Archimedes

Architecture
Columns
- Doric style
- Iconic style

Olympic Games
- When?
- Where?
- What?

New ways of thinking
- Invented democracy (What is democracy?)
- Organized city states
  - Athens
  - Sparta
- Introduced law processes (trial by jury)

Don't forget to make it interesting!
Snappy introduction
Headings
Pictures and diagrams (label different bits)
Fun features: facts in thought bubbles, etc.

Iron Age Celts

Plan an information report about life in Iron Age Britain. Use your ideas to create a non-chronological report.

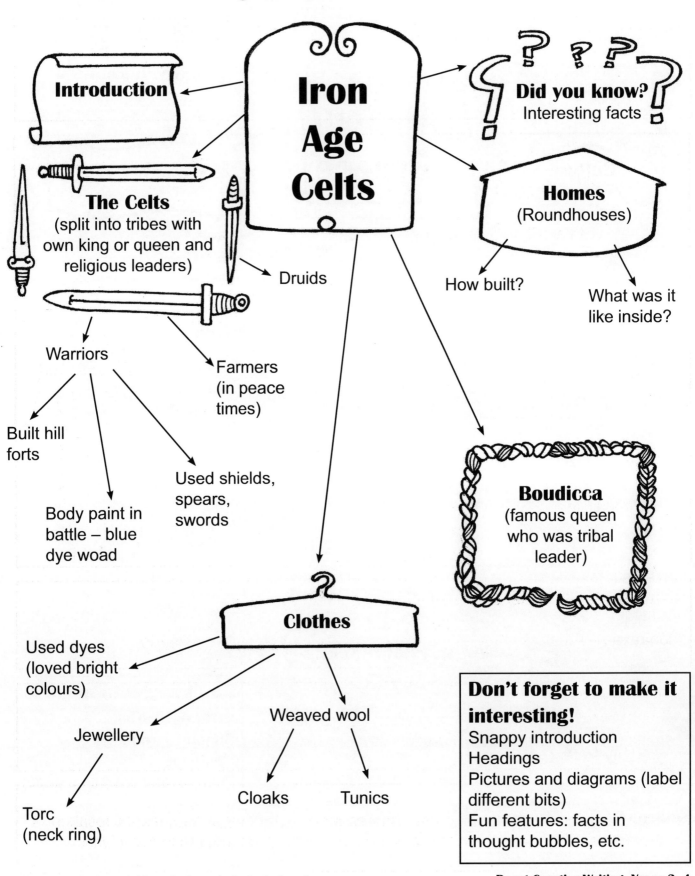

Introduction

Iron Age Celts

Did you know?
Interesting facts

The Celts
(split into tribes with own king or queen and religious leaders)

Druids

Homes
(Roundhouses)

How built?

What was it like inside?

Warriors

Farmers (in peace times)

Built hill forts

Used shields, spears, swords

Body paint in battle – blue dye woad

Boudicca
(famous queen who was tribal leader)

Clothes

Used dyes (loved bright colours)

Weaved wool

Jewellery

Cloaks

Tunics

Torc (neck ring)

Don't forget to make it interesting!
Snappy introduction
Headings
Pictures and diagrams (label different bits)
Fun features: facts in thought bubbles, etc.

Boost Creative Writing, Years 3–4
© Judith Thornby and Brilliant Publications

My newspaper report

Write a **different version** of the story of Red Riding Hood as a newspaper report. Change the story so that the Wolf is the Goodie and Red Riding Hood is the Baddie.

Headline: Grab the reader's attention – make it interesting!

Idea: **Wolf only trying to help!**

Report the facts

Remember, in your version Red Riding Hood is the Baddie and the Wolf is the Goodie.

Answer the questions:

❀ Where did Red Riding Hood live?
❀ What was not very nice about her character? Why?
❀ What was she told to do?
❀ Where did the Wolf see her? Why did he follow her?
❀ How did he lose sight of her?
❀ What made the Wolf stop at Granny's house? Why was Granny upset?
❀ Why did the Wolf go into Granny's house? How did he help Granny?
❀ When Red Riding Hood arrived, what did she do to upset Granny?
❀ Why did the Wolf chase Red Riding Hood?

Reported by ....

For.. (name of newspaper)

Use quotes

Ideas: What did the woodcutter say when he arrived?
I spoke to the woodcutter and he said that…

Vocabulary
cottage, woods, selfish, spoilt, cross, temper, tantrum, mother, asked, take, cupcakes, dropped, disappeared, passed, saw, helped, rude, only, wanted, teach her a lesson

---

My newspaper report

Reporter:

Boost Creative Writing, Years 3–4
© Judith Thornby and Brilliant Publications

How to make pancakes

Instructional writing

The pancake instructions are all mixed up.
Can you put them in the correct order?
The ingredients should be in the order they
are used in the recipe.

What to do	You will need
Crack an egg into bowl.	an egg
Place on a plate and enjoy with sugar and lemon.	cup of milk
Whisk batter until smooth.	cup of flour
Cook for a minute and flip over; fry until golden.	knob of butter
Add flour and milk to the egg to make a batter.	frying pan
Spoon $\frac{1}{2}$ small cup of batter into the pan.	sugar
Melt a knob of butter in the frying pan.	lemon

Make a super sandwich

Write instructions for making a super sandwich.

Bossy words (imperative words)

Get	Squeeze
Spread	Place
Add	Press (together)
Slice	Cut (in half)
Chop	Eat
Grate	Enjoy
Sprinkle	

More vocabulary

brown bread, butter, margarine, cream cheese, cheese, ham, chicken, lettuce, cucumber, crisps, jelly, tomato ketchup, brown sauce, salad cream, pieces, slices, knife, plate

Boost Creative Writing, Years 3–4
© Judith Thornby and Brilliant Publications

The clever trick

The Enormous Crocodile was cross with the Roly Poly bird for spoiling his trick. He waddled off into the jungle to think of another plan.

A little while later... where did he play his next trick?
Ideas:

at the funfair   at the school   in the jungle

What did he pretend to be? How did he disguise himself?

Ideas:
cuddly crocodile prize at the fun fair … which stall?
orange tree
bookshelf at school

What did the children do?

Who warned the children? How?
Remember to use speech marks and start a new line for each new speaker.

Ideas:
Humpy Rumpy the elephant, Trunky the elephant, Muggle Wump the monkey

---

How did the Enormous Crocodile feel?
Did he wonder what he could do for his next trick?

Vocabulary: absolutely furious, a great big sulk

The clever trick

Plan another clever trick that the Clever Crocodile might play using the story mountain format.

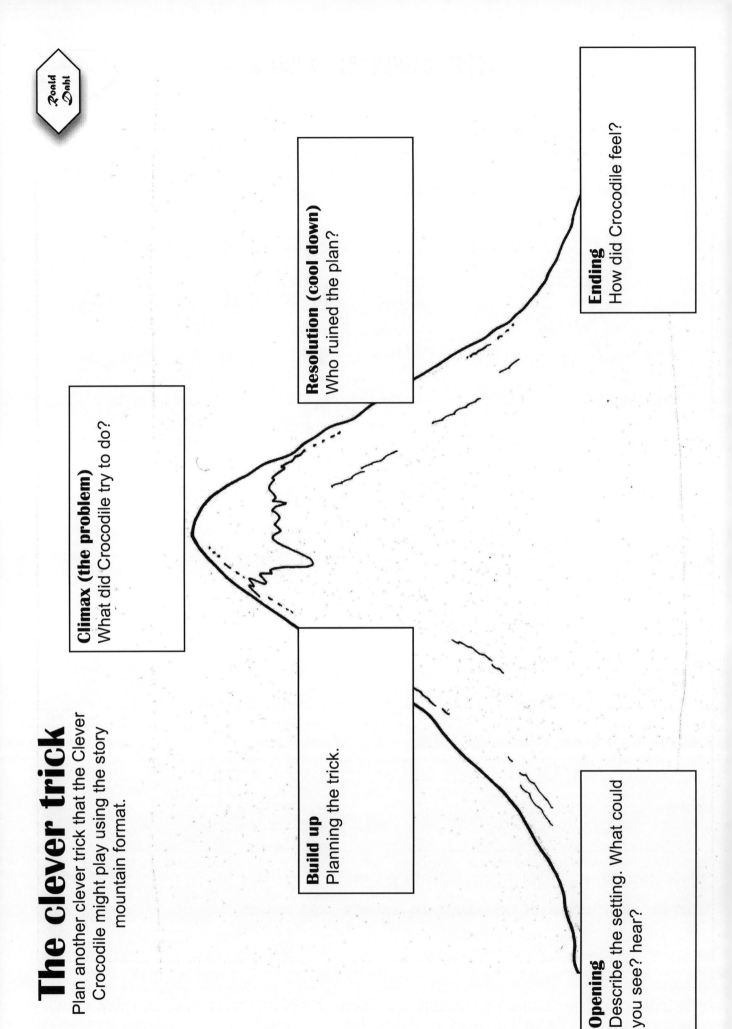

Climax (the problem)
What did Crocodile try to do?

Resolution (cool down)
Who ruined the plan?

Ending
How did Crocodile feel?

Build up
Planning the trick.

Opening
Describe the setting. What could you see? hear?

Roald Dahl

Boost Creative Writing, Years 3–4
© Judith Thornby and Brilliant Publications

Mr Twit's trick

What does Mr Twit look like?

Draw and label a picture of Mr Twit. Use powerful adjectives to describe him.

Vocabulary

beard, eyebrows, face, bristles, nostrils, ear holes, tufts of hair, tongue, thick, spiky, dirty, smelly, mouldy, foul, revolting, horrible, disgusting

Boost Creative Writing, Years 3–4
© Judith Thornby and Brilliant Publications

Mr Twit's trick

Put a short draft of your main ideas into each box using the story mountain format.

Climax (the problem)
Playing the trick.

Resolution (cool down)
Results of the trick.

Build up
Planning the trick.

Ending
Promise of revenge.

Opening
Describe Mr Twit's character (look at your picture to help).

Boost Creative Writing, Years 3–4
© Judith Thornby and Brilliant Publications

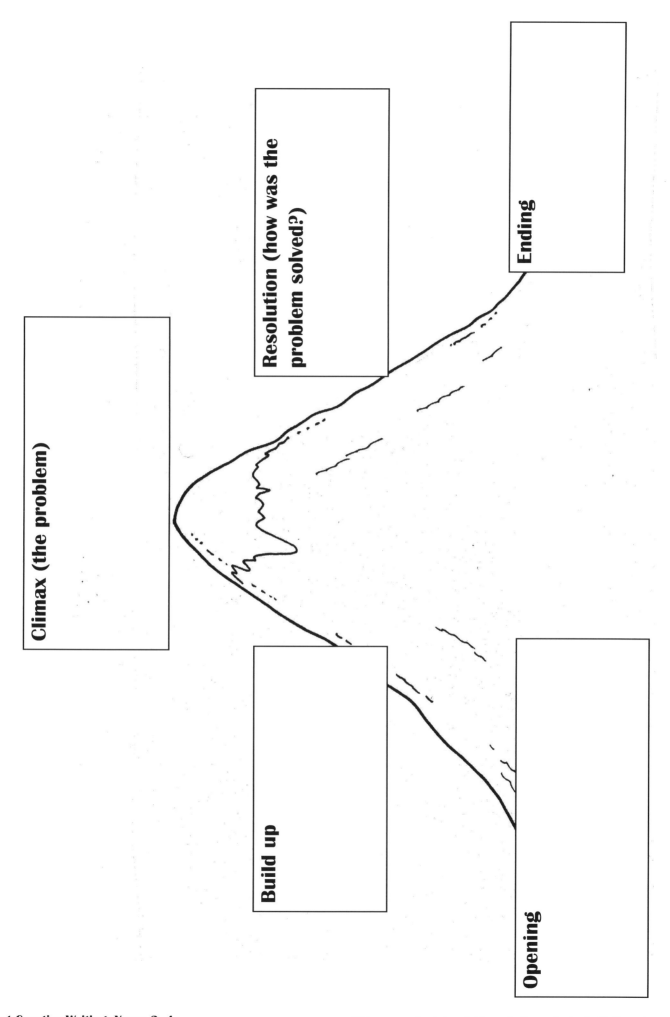

Climax (the problem)

Resolution (how was the problem solved?)

Ending

Build up

Opening

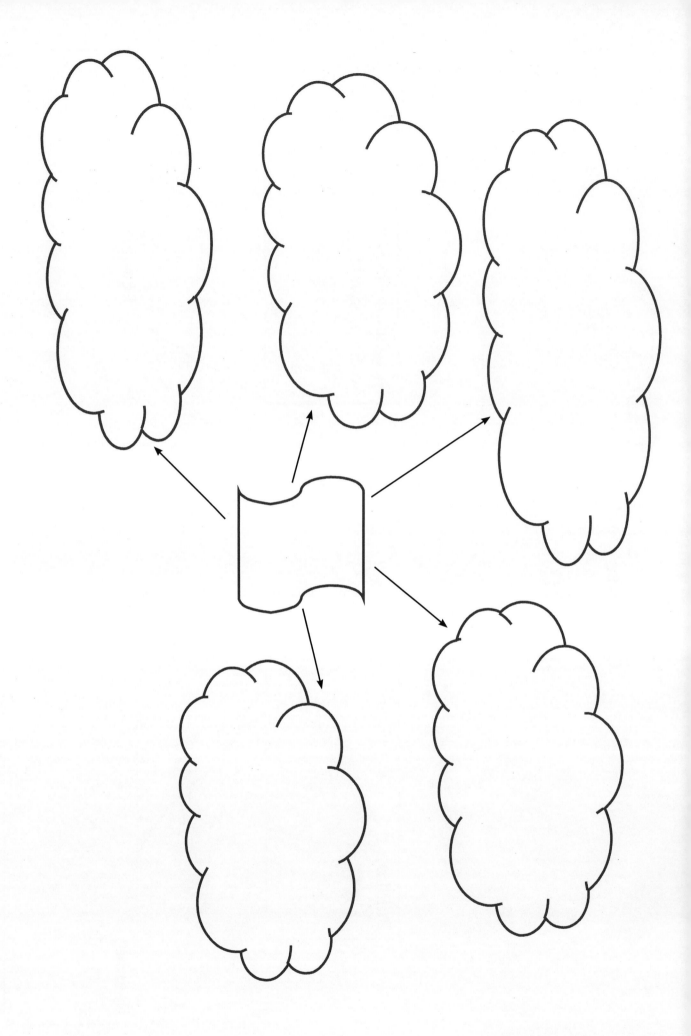

Boost Creative Writing, Years 3–4
© Judith Thornby and Brilliant Publications